TONY VALENTE

CONTENTS

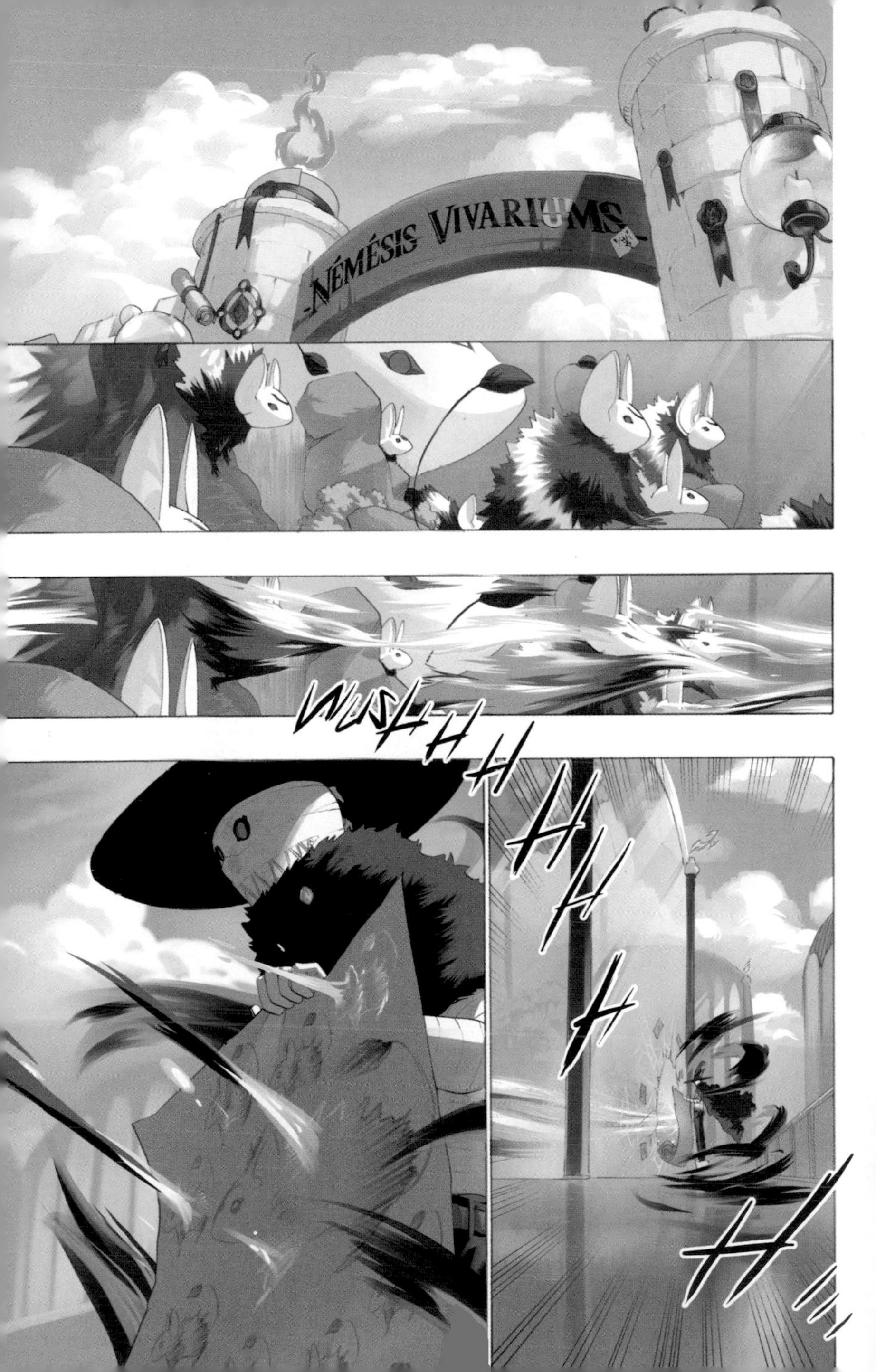

NÉMÉSIS VIVARIUMS

WUSH

H H H
H H
H
H

CHAPTER 77
BROOM BROOM CUP SURVIVAL #2

AND IT'S HEADED STRAIGHT FOR TEAM 5!

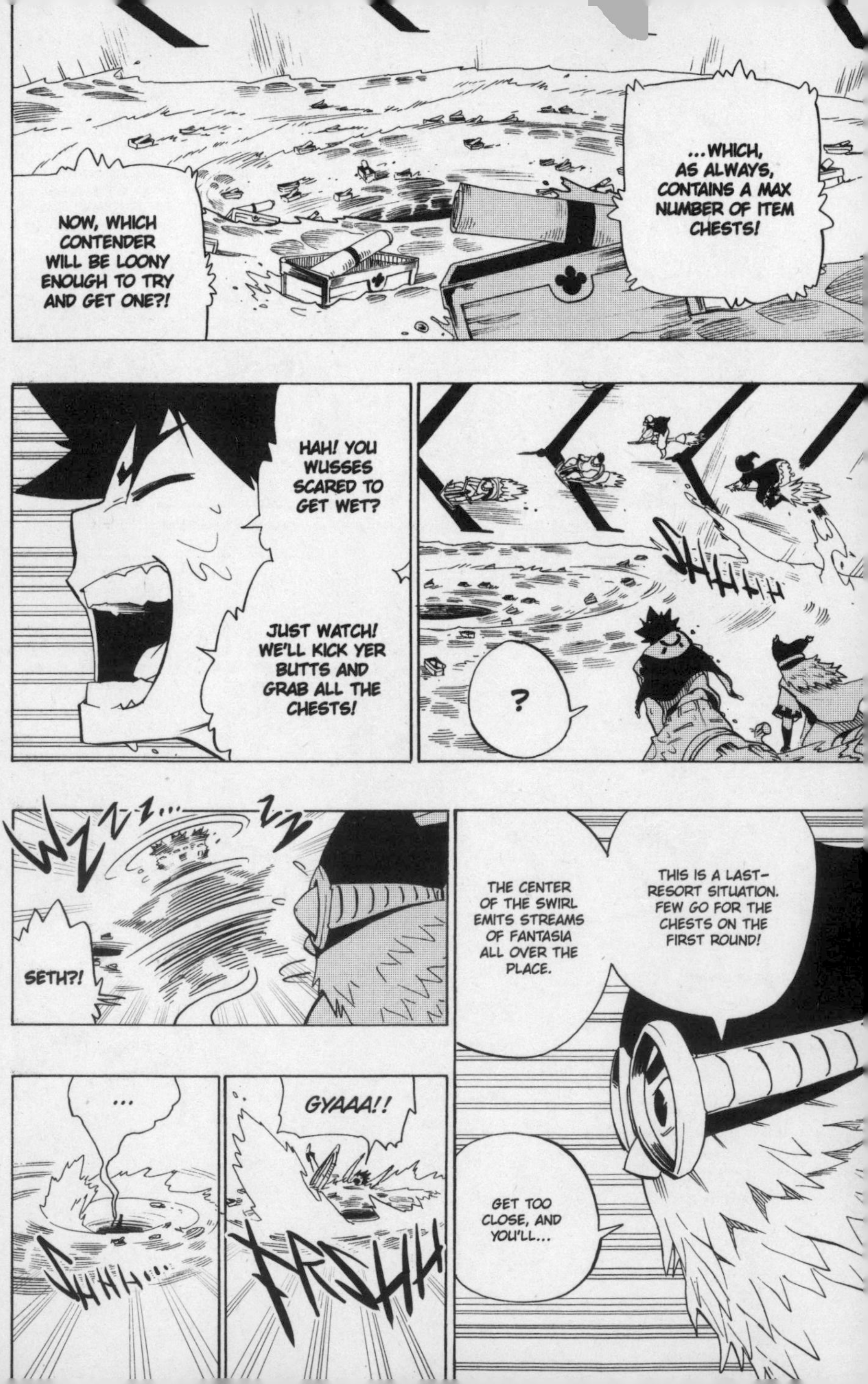

NOW, WHICH CONTENDER WILL BE LOONY ENOUGH TO TRY AND GET ONE?!

...WHICH, AS ALWAYS, CONTAINS A MAX NUMBER OF ITEM CHESTS!

HAH! YOU WUSSES SCARED TO GET WET?

JUST WATCH! WE'LL KICK YER BUTTS AND GRAB ALL THE CHESTS!

?

WZZZZ... ZZ

SETH?!

...

GYAAA!!

THE CENTER OF THE SWIRL EMITS STREAMS OF FANTASIA ALL OVER THE PLACE.

THIS IS A LAST-RESORT SITUATION. FEW GO FOR THE CHESTS ON THE FIRST ROUND!

GET TOO CLOSE, AND YOU'LL...

I WAS GONNA SAY WE HAD TO CHECK THE DIRECTION THE GATE'S EARS WERE IN!

WE GOT PUSHED BACK? HOW'D THAT HAPPEN?!

IT HAPPENED 'CAUSE YOU WOULDN'T LET ME FINISH TALKIN'!

BUT THE RINGS ARE TURNABLE... AND THE EAR ON THE LEFT SIDE SENDS US BACK IN REVERSE!

IF THE BENT EAR IS ON THE RIGHT SIDE, YOU'LL ACCELERATE!

BUT WE'RE WAY BEHIND...

SURE, NOW THAT I'VE EXPLAINED IT!

RIGHT, SOUNDS EASY ENOUGH...

SO WE GOTTA AVOID PASSING 'EM, OKAY?!

STAY CLOSE TO ME!

AND MAKE SURE TO GRAB A SCROLL!

THAT'S THE PRICE OF MESSING UP!

WE CAN COME BACK THOUGH.

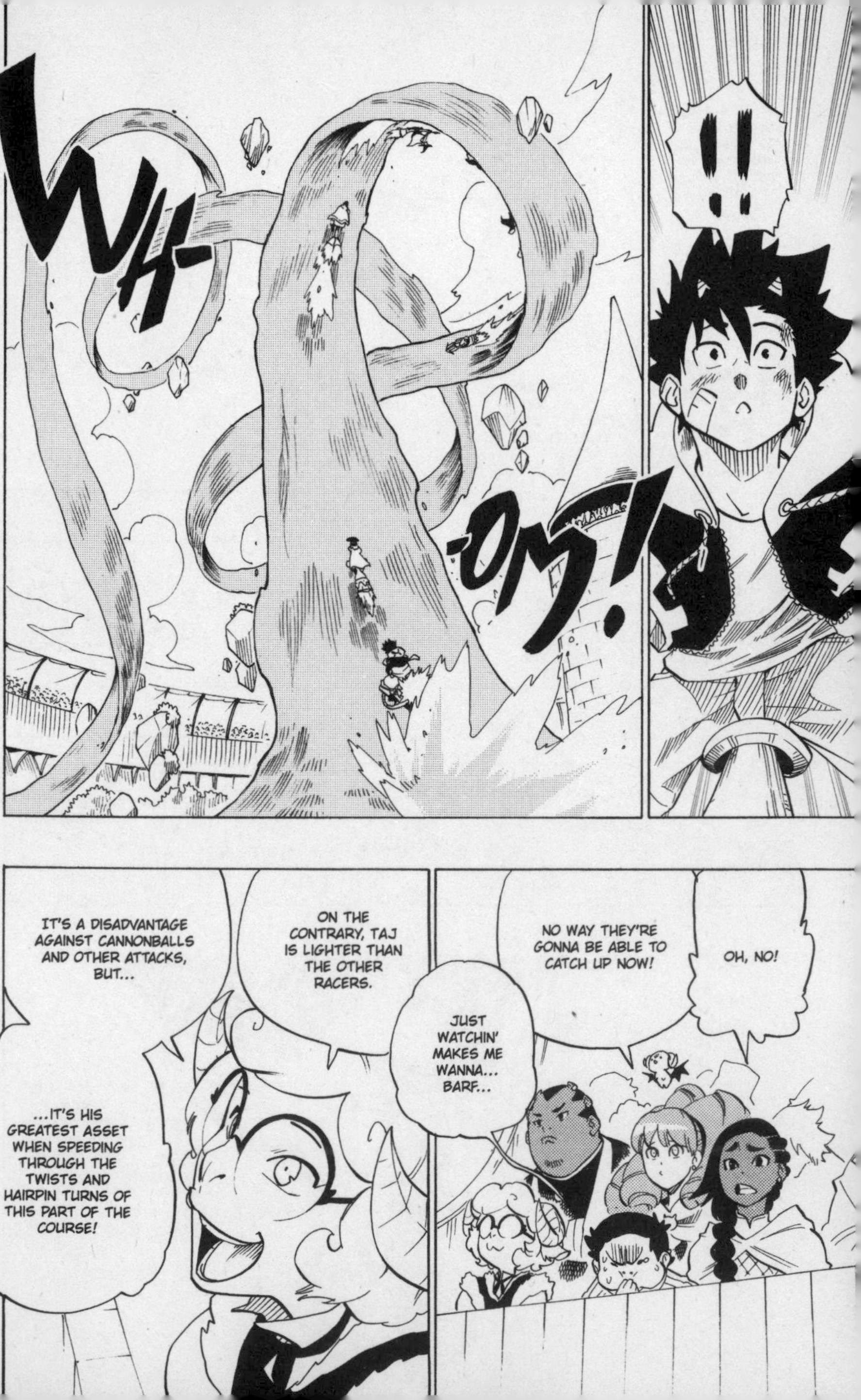

...BUT YOU'RE NOT EVEN TRYING TO WIN!

I SPENT ALL MY MONEY ON THIS RACE...

NO! YOU SCREWED EVERYTHING UP!!

EVEN SHOWING UP THAT DICKOLAS GUY DOESN'T MOTIVATE ME ALL THAT MUCH!

ALL THAT COMPETITIVENESS, TRYING TO GO FASTER THAN ANYONE ELSE... I JUST DON'T SEE THE POINT!

BASICALLY, YEAH!

THAT ALL WE'RE GOOD FOR IS FIGHTING!

IF YOU WON'T TRY, THEN THAT'S SAYING EVERYONE WHO SNEERS AT IS INFECTED IS RIGHT!

OKAY, THEN WHAT **WOULD** MOTIVATE YOU? A SMACK IN THE FACE?!

WELL, MAYBE...

I JUST WISH I COULD REALLY GIVE THEM ONE...

LOOK AT ALL THOSE PEOPLE! THEY WANT A SHOW!

FANTASIA IS CRAZY! AND HAS SUCH POSSIBILITIES!
I DON'T WANNA JUST FIGHT AND HUNT NEMESES!
IF I DID, MY FOLKS'D GET CRAZY WORRIED!
SO I WANNA SHOW 'EM...
THEN MAYBE EVEN MY MOM AND POP WOULDN'T BE AS NERVOUS ABOUT ME BEING A WIZARD!
MY PARENTS AND EVERYONE ELSE...
OUTSIDE OF THE ARTEMIS... ALL OVER PHARÉNOS...
I WANNA SHOW THOSE PEOPLE THAT ALL THIS WIZARDRY... THAT THEY DON'T HAVE TO BE SCARED OF US INFECTED!
THAT SOME OF US ARE EVEN WORTH ADMIRING!

CHAPTER 78

FINISH LINE

AND SEVENTH, RUAN OF TEAM 4!
OH, BUT WAIT...
BSHH
IN SEVENTH, JEAN-PEDROVITCH FROM TEAM 5!
SETH IS TENACIOUS, GOTTA SAY!
BUT HOW'S HE GONNA DO THE ROLLER COASTER WITHOUT HIS BROOM?
MY BROOM...
SWIM REAL FAST?
OH!
AND NOW SETH IS SHOWING OFF HIS WATERSKIING SKILLS!

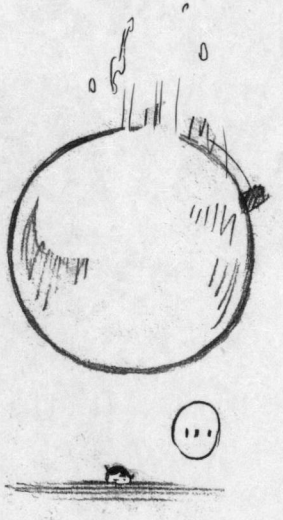

OKAY, NOBODY AROUND TO DUNK ME AGAIN?

CHAPTER 79

MARRY ME BABY

TEAM 5!

LADIES AND GENTS...

A ROUND OF APPLAUSE FOR THE WINNERS OF THIS 258TH BROOM BROOM SURVIVAL CUP...

AND TEAM 4!

WH-

'OM

TEAM 3!

EVERYBODY WINS!

AND ALSO TEAMS 2 AND 1!

TEAM 2
(ELBOW)

TEAM 5
(FOREHEAD)

TEAM 4
(BUTT)

TEAM 1
(HEAD)

TEAM 3
(FOREHEAD)

REPLAY

...YOU ARE!
ALL THE TEAMS
FINISHED AT
THE EXACT
SAME TIME!

HMPH!
I REFUSE
TO SHARE
THE STAGE
WITH THESE
BUFFOONS!

LIKE IT OR NOT,
MR. NICK...

THIS RACE
ISN'T ABOUT
INDIVIDUAL
RESULTS!

TAJ WON
FOR HIS
ENTIRE
TEAM!

RATIONALIZING
MUCH?!

HU HU
HU!

HA
HA
HA!

HAH! I
PASSED
THE FINISH
LINE AHEAD
OF JEAN-
PEDROVITCH!

I SO BEAT
THAT UPSTART!

YOU GAVE
US A SHOW
LIKE NONE
WE'VE EVER
SEEN!

SO I MUST
CONGRATULATE MY
ROYAL ME-NESS FOR
COMING UP WITH THIS
GAME IN THE FIRST
PLACE!

THAT'S FINE.

LET TAJ HAVE
THE GLORY. HE
MORE THAN
DESERVES IT!

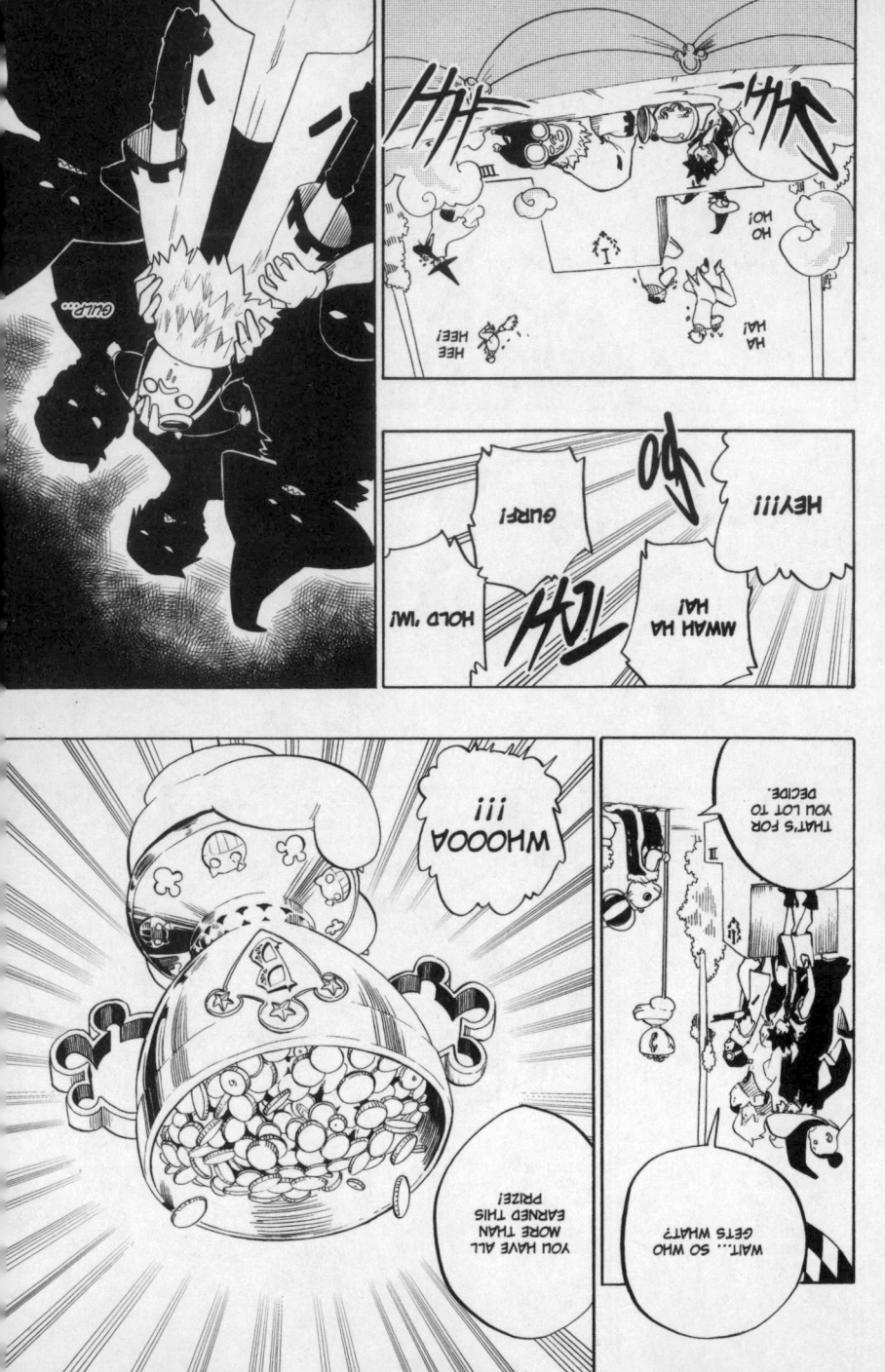

MAN! EVEN WHEN I WIN, I LOSE!

YOU WERE RIGHT, SETH... COMPETING ISN'T WORTH CRAP!

WHAT'S THE POINT OF EVEN GO—

THOSE GUYS WERE CRAZY!

EMPTY! CLEANED OUT!

PRETTY SURE ONE OF 'EM BIT ME!

RE PAK

!!

MAYBE I'M JUST NOT MADE FOR...

WHAT GIVES?! I SAID I AGREE WITH YOU!

PAK

AAAGH!!!

BUT YOU DO!

WHO SAID HE DIDN'T SEE THE POINT OF IT.

STOP IT! YOU'RE THE ONE WHO—

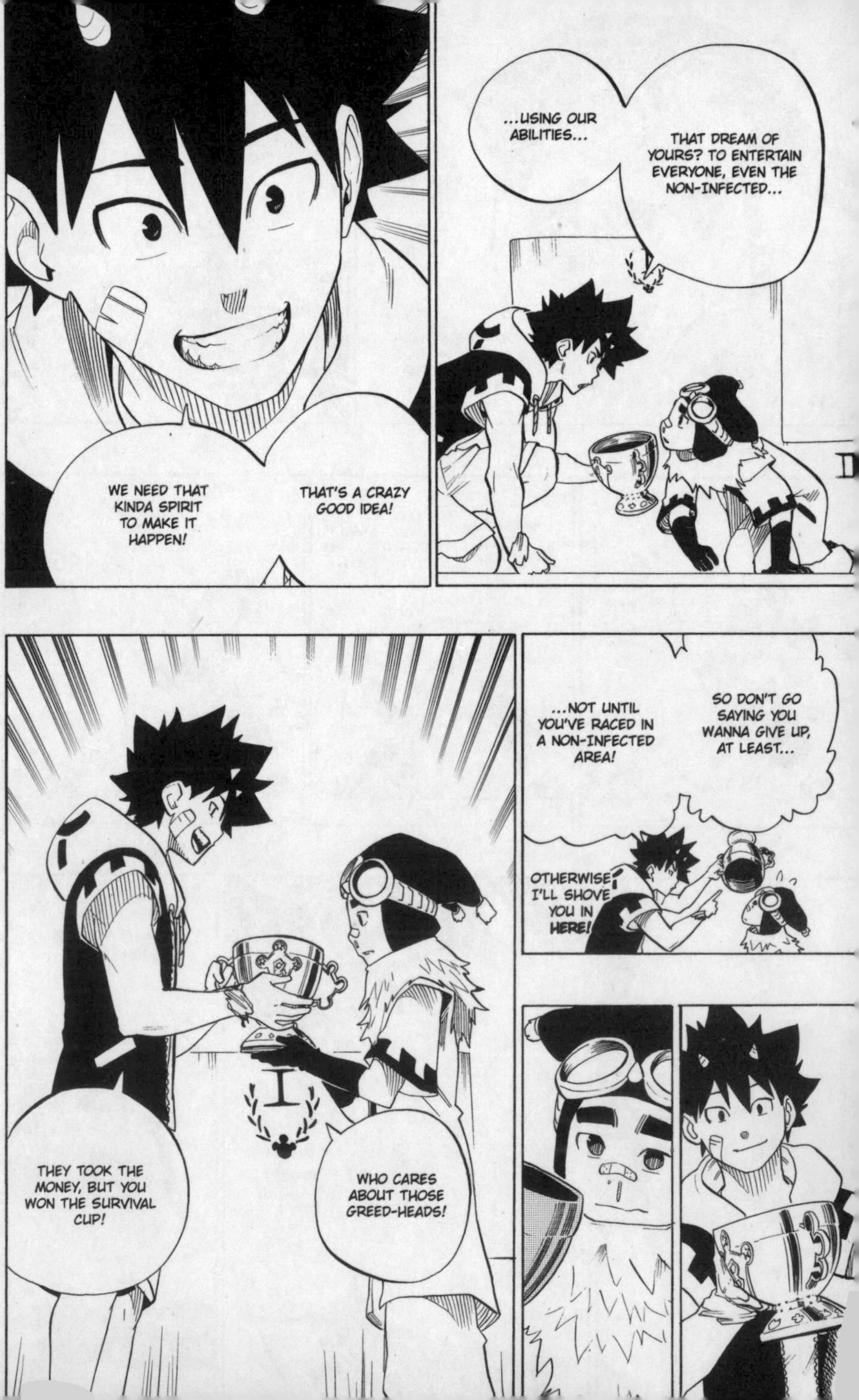

I WON, DIDN'T I...

YEAH...

SPO

HELPING OTHERS TO FOLLOW A PATH YOU HAVE NO INTEREST IN YOURSELF!

REMINDS ME OF MY FIRST ORDERS AS KING.

WEEEELL... NO.

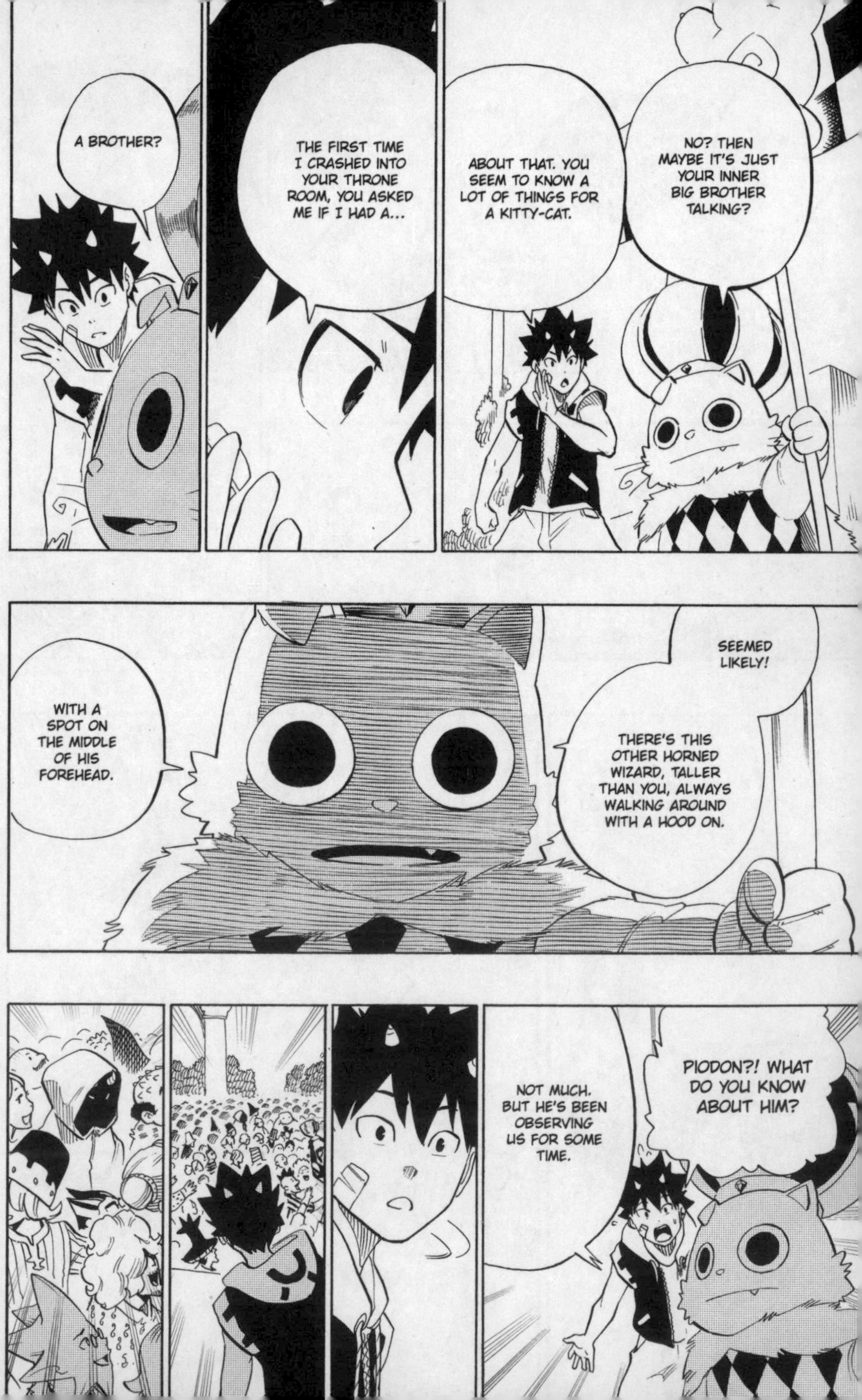

BAAA?
ON SECOND THOUGHT, MAYBE THAT'S NOT HIM...
LOOKS MORE LIKE YOUR SISTER.
JOIN ME IN THE CASTLE IN ABOUT AN HOUR. BRING YOUR CREW.
WE'VE GOT BUSINESS.

MLM
AND YOU REALLY HAVE NO IDEA WHY WE'RE HERE?
HOW LONG DO WE HAVE TO WAIT?
HMM...?
OH, HELLO MY DEAR BIRDIES.
!!
HE'S BEEN UP THERE NAPPING?!
NAPPING? NO, NOT ME! NO WAY!

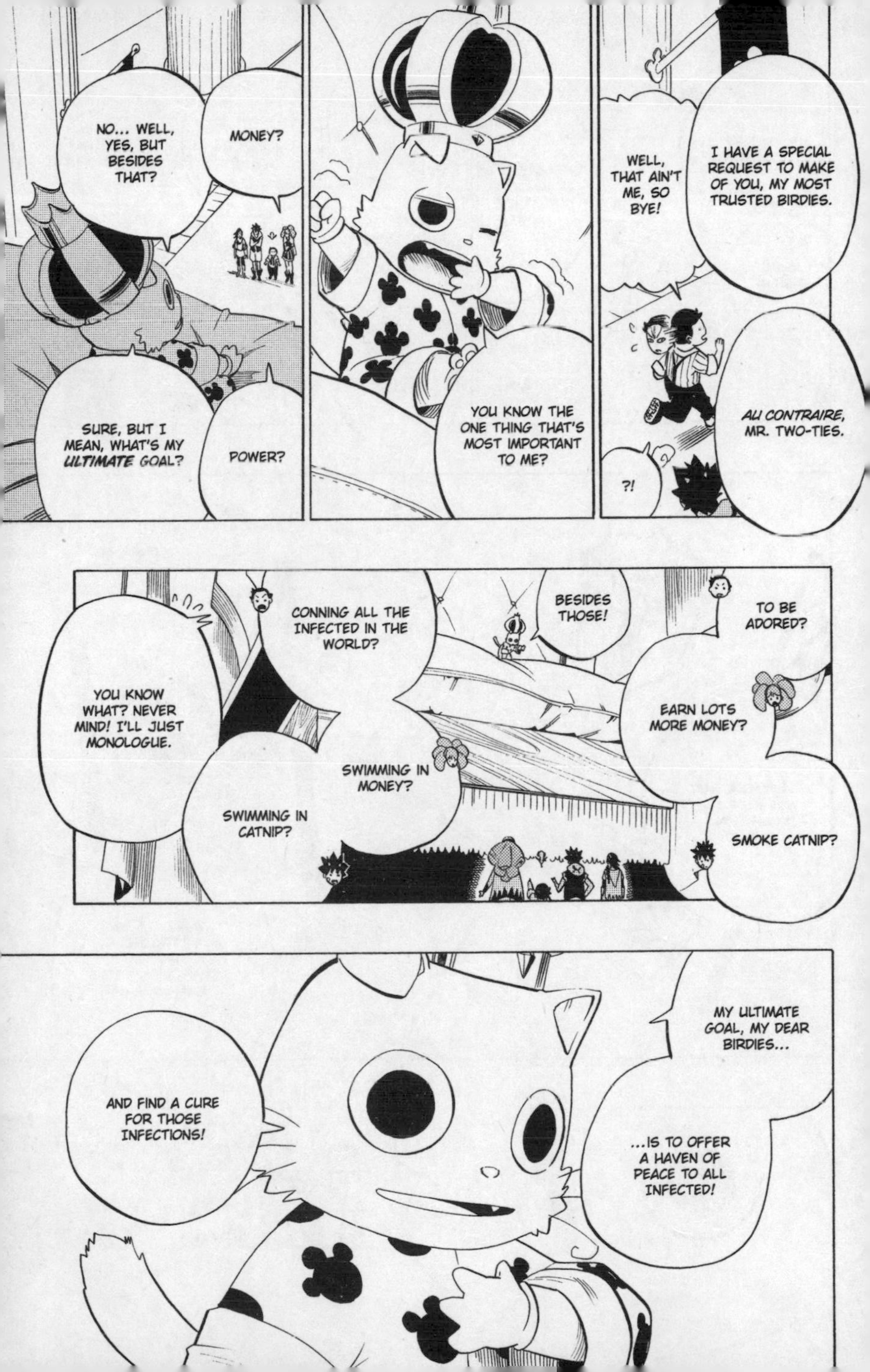
I HAVE A SPECIAL REQUEST TO MAKE OF YOU, MY MOST TRUSTED BIRDIES.
WELL, THAT AIN'T ME, SO BYE!
AU CONTRAIRE, MR. TWO-TIES.
?!
YOU KNOW THE ONE THING THAT'S MOST IMPORTANT TO ME?
MONEY?
NO... WELL, YES, BUT BESIDES THAT?
POWER?
SURE, BUT I MEAN, WHAT'S MY *ULTIMATE* GOAL?
TO BE ADORED?
BESIDES THOSE!
EARN LOTS MORE MONEY?
SMOKE CATNIP?
CONNING ALL THE INFECTED IN THE WORLD?
SWIMMING IN MONEY?
SWIMMING IN CATNIP?
YOU KNOW WHAT? NEVER MIND! I'LL JUST MONOLOGUE.
MY ULTIMATE GOAL, MY DEAR BIRDIES...
...IS TO OFFER A HAVEN OF PEACE TO ALL INFECTED!
AND FIND A CURE FOR THOSE INFECTIONS!

AND YOU... YOU RECEIVED THE HONORARY TITLE OF WIZARD-MITE.

KNIGHT! WIZARD-KNIGHT!

THE TWO OF YOU ARE IN GOOD STANDING WITH HER SUBLIME MAJESTY, QUEEN BOADICÉE.

I AM SURE YOU WOULD BE ABLE TO CONVINCE HER TO ACCEPT!

CONSIDERING THE PLACE YOU HOLD IN HER MAJESTY'S HEART...

SOMETHING ABOUT THAT SCROLL...

SHLIN

BZ

AND YOU, PRINCESS...

WELCOME TO MY HUMBLE KINGDOM!

NOW, NOW! I AM TALKING ABOUT AN ALLIANCE THAT WOULD BENEFIT US ALL!

ACCEPT... YOU MEAN, THE ALLIANCE?

WHOA THERE, KITTY! WE KNOW HOW THOSE CONTRACTS OF YOURS GO!

BUT NOT A POLITICAL ALLIANCE.

...STASHED WITH THE REST OF THE MARRIAGE PROPOSALS SHE RECEIVES EACH WEEK.

I'VE SEEN THAT SAME SCROLL IN THE QUEEN'S CHAMBER...

...

TcHK

FWIj

Marry Me Baby!

YOU THINK I...

NOT SURE I BELIEVE YOU.

I'M SERIOUS.

ALL RIGHT, I ADMIT IT, YES...

BUT I'M ONLY THINKING OF THE WELFARE OF OUR PEOPLE.

I'VE EVEN BUILT EVERYTHING HERE TO HER SCALE!

EVERY...

...THING!

EH... REMEMBER, INFECTIONS AREN'T HEREDITARY...

MROWRR!

HSSSS!

MEW!

HI HI!

SHE'D BE PAMPERED, SPOILED...

WE'D SPEND OUR DAYS IN UNALLOYED BLISS, TENDING OUR PROGENY!

WE'LL DROP THEM A POSTCARD.

HAH! SOME ALLIANCE!

PEOPLE? I DON'T KNOW WHAT YOU...

OH, RIGHT, THE PEOPLE!

AND THE QUEEN WOULD NEVER LEAVE HER PEOPLE.

I CAME TO WARN THE KID AND HIS BAND OF BROTHERS.

THEY DIDN'T THIS TIME. AND I AIN'T TALKIN' TO YOU, KITTY.

ABOUT WHAT?

THAT IS, I PAY HANDSOMELY TO DEAL WITH EMERGENCIES.

THERE'S A SECURITY SERVICE THAT I EXPLOI...

YOUR NEMESES...

THEY'VE VANISHED FROM THE VIVARIUMS!

NÉMÉSIS VIVARIUMS

WOW... ALL GONE.

THERE'S NO ESCAPIN' THE VIVARIUMS.

LOOK AT ALL THE SPELLS THAT WERE KEEPIN' 'EM IN.

THE NEMESES! WHY'D YOU THINK THEY ESCAPED?!

TO GET REVENGE ON US!

WHO ARE YOU TALKING TO, DOC?

IT WAS THEIR IDEA TO CAPTURE YOU! I'M INNOCENT!

SO HOW'D THEY GET AWAY?

BAAAAAAA!

A MYSTERIOUS HORNED WIZARD...

Chapter 80

Disillusioned

AN ILLUSION!

I ONLY SAW IT DUE TO MY SHAMAN VISION.

THERE WAS NOTHING TO SENSE. THESE ILLUSION SPELLS WERE TOO POWERFUL...

WATCH IT...

SORRY. YOU KINDA SUCK, SIR!

AND YOU DIDN'T SENSE IT?

YOU KINDA SUCK, DON'T YOU.

MAYBE SOMEONE AIMING TO SELL THEM?

OR MAYBE A DOMITOR?

WHO'D POSSIBLY WANT TO KIDNAP A BUNCH OF NEMESES?

IF THOSE NEMESES ARE OUT THERE BEING USED TO CAUSE MAYHEM...
...IT'LL BE MY FAULT!
I CAN'T LET IT HAPPEN!
WHAT?! I'M NO KNI-
A KNIGHT SHOULD NOT FLEE ADVERSITY!
AH, CRAP, I AM!
LATERS!
IT IS YOUR FAULT.
SO, GOOD LUCK!
SEE YA!
YOU'RE RIGHT...
AND I CAN'T GET INSIDE WIZARDS' HEADS LIKE THE PRINCESS THERE!
BUT I AIN'T GOT THE REDHEAD'S TRACKER SKILLS!
NOT TO MENTION THAT GUYS METAVISION!

FLHH

?

THEY DON'T NEED ME!

US THREE, WE SHOULD BE ABLE TO HANDLE THIS!

ACTUALLY, THE OLD KID'S NOT WRONG...

GYSON!!

HUH?

AH! SEE?

I DON'T FOLLOW...

WE TAKE ADVANTAGE OF OUR COMBINED STRENGTHS!

THAT'S RIGHT!

MÉLIE! IN THE CAILLTE FOREST, YOU USED A SPELL TO REVEAL MYR'S STEPS...

...WHICH ENABLED US FIND SETH!

I'VE GOT TRACE FANTASIA HERE, BUT IT'S VERY VAGUE AND... IMPERSONAL!

THERE ARE SPELLS BLURRING THE IDENTITY OF ANY WIZARDS WHO WERE HERE.

VESTIGIA REVELARE!

WUSH!

OKAY, SURE, HIGHNESS...

KEEP TRYING!

SETH! GET THAT SHAMAN VISION WORKING!

SEE! I KNEW IT!

SETH'S SHAMAN VISION'S MAKING THE FANTASIA TAKE A FORM MÉLIE CAN TRACK!

AWRIGHT! LET'S SEE OUR THIEF...

BZ00M

AT LEAST THAT'S WHAT MÉLIE TOLD ME. BOOBRIE AND I WERE STUCK IN A COFFIN AT THE TIME.

...THEN-BAM!- TORQUE APPEARS AND-SLASH!-BYE BYE DOMITOR.

THEN SETH TURNED INTO HIS "RHAAARR!" MODE.

JWURZ

HER? WHAT ABOUT ME?!

SNIFFF... POOR HAMELINE!

HE ALWAYS HAS A GOOD REASON FOR WHAT HE DOES, SETH.

REMEMBER WHEN HE ATTACKED US IN RUMBLE TOWN?

GRIMM...

WHAT WOULD MAKE HIM DO THIS?!

...HE WAS PROTECTING THEM FROM KONRAD, WHO'D HAVE KILLED THEM TO KEEP THE DOMITOR'S PRESENCE A SECRET!

AND WHEN HE WAS KIDNAPPING ALL THOSE WHO'D COME FACE TO FACE WITH THE NEMESES...

HE MISTOOK US FOR NEMESIS TAMERS!

THIS WOULDN'T BE THE FIRST TIME WE MISREAD HIM.

IF YOU'D ALL LISTENED TO ME FROM THE START...

OR MAYBE WE'VE BEING NAIVE TO THINK HE WAS EVER OUR ALLY.

KEEP FLYING LOW, KIDS!

AN INQUISITION PATROL SHIP!

ARE THEY HOSTILE TO INFECTED?

STAY ALERT NOW! WE'RE ENTERING THE ESTRIE KINGDOMS.

NOT HOSTILE, NO, BUT YOU MIGHT NOT WANT TO FLAUNT YOUR BROOM.

A SIMPLE IDENTITY CHECK COULD WIND UP TURNING NASTY.

WAIT, YAGA...

ESPECIALLY IF YOU'RE SEEN FLYING WITH US. RIGHT, KID?

OVER THERE! SOMETHING'S WATCHING US!

I DON'T SEE ANYTHING!

ME NEITHER! NUH-UH!

OH?

YOU IMAGINING THINGS, HORNS?

UP AHEAD!!

UH... UH... UP!

NO! THERE WAS SOMETHING OVER THERE!

SETH! BEHIND YOU!

SETH!

CHAPTER 81

THE MESNIE

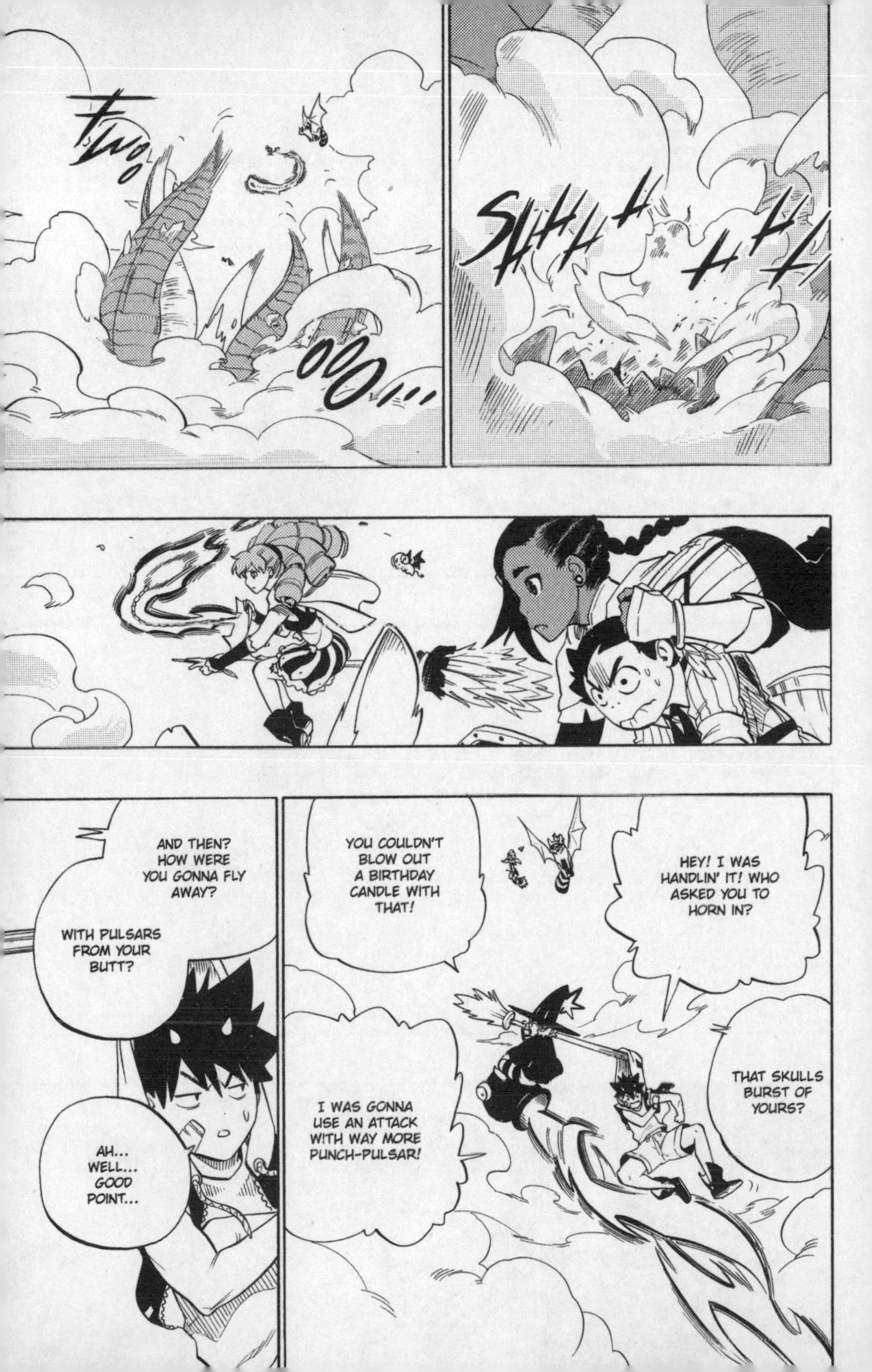

AND THEN? HOW WERE YOU GONNA FLY AWAY?

YOU COULDN'T BLOW OUT A BIRTHDAY CANDLE WITH THAT!

HEY! I WAS HANDLIN' IT! WHO ASKED YOU TO HORN IN?

WITH PULSARS FROM YOUR BUTT?

I WAS GONNA USE AN ATTACK WITH WAY MORE PUNCH-PULSAR!

THAT SKULLS BURST OF YOURS?

AH... WELL... GOOD POINT...

IT WAS A CREATURE FROM BELOW. THEY COME UP HERE EVERY SO OFTEN.

THEY USUALLY DON'T SHOW THEMSELVES UNLESS DISTURBED.

WE CAN AGREE THIS WAS **NOT** A NEMESIS, RIGHT?

ANY THEORIES, GUYS?

WEIRD, THOUGH... IT FELT LIKE IT WAS DELIBERATELY COMING AFTER US!

LIKE WHEN AN AIRSHIP SINKS...

...OR WHEN A CARGO SHIP LOSES A LOAD.

...

IT WANTED TO TENDERIZE ME SO I'D BE EASY TO EAT!

IT WAS AFTER ME! ME! I KNOW IT!

THERE ARE A COUPLE OF LIKELY PLACES...
BUT AS THIS GRIMM GUY IS FLYING AROUND WITH A GROUP OF THOSE CREATURES...
...I BET HE IS GOING STRAIGHT TO THE NEMESIS DOMITORS...
...IN BÔME.
I STILL HAVE TO FIND HIM!

OR THROW OURSELVES INTO A LIVE VOLCANO!

I CAN RATTLE OFF ZILLIONS OF FASTER WAYS OF SNUFFING OURSELVES!

WHILE WE'RE AT IT, WHY DON'T WE JUST CONTRACT THE PLAGUE AND DIE ALREADY!

YEAH, LET'S HEAD STRAIGHT FOR THE LAND OF ENCHANTMENT RULED BY INQUISITORS AND DOMITORS!

NOPE! FORGET IT! YOU'RE NOT GOING SOLO AGAIN!

GRACK!

OKAY!

YOU GUYS DON'T HAVE TO COME...

I JUST SAID I WAS GOING.

I WANT TO UNDERSTAND WHY THEY'RE SO SCARED OF INFECTED!

I GREW UP IN A COUNTRY WHERE WIZARDS ARE PAMPERED... SO I WANT TO SEE BŌME.

AND AS CROWN PRINCESS OF CYFANDIR, I AIM TO CHECK OUT EVERY CORNER OF THE WORLD!

SO THE QUEEN HERSELF SAID!

ALRIGHTY, THEN! SEE YA LA...

AAAAH!

POK

WORD OF ADVICE! DON'T FLY STRAIGHT AHEAD FOR TOO LONG!

DRAGONS AND FOLKS ON FLYING BROOMS EVENTUALLY DRAW ATTENTION AROUND HERE!

I'LL LEAVE YOU HERE, LITTLE BUDDIES!

WOW! THIS IT GETTIN' TOO SAPPY FOR ME!

HEY!

WHY CAN'T I GO WITH HIM?!

THANKS, YAGA!

JUST GRAB ON TO THE SIDE OF AN AIRSHIP.

YOU'LL AVOID BEING SPOTTED BY PATROLS AND SHOULD GET TO BÔME UNHASSLED.

YAGA HERE. ANYONE FROM THE COVEN RECEIVING?

YAGI-BOO, IT'S BEEN TOO LONG!

HMPH! JUST YOU TWO? SPECS AND BEARD GUY?

HEY! YAGA, YOU LI'L SPROUT! HOW YA DOIN'?

...BUT YOU DON'T HEAR ME YAPPIN' ABOUT IT!

YEAH? WELL, I TOOK THE LIBERTY OF TEACHING HIM SHAMAN VISION AND WHATNOT...

NEVER MIND. GOT SOME NEWS...

TOOK THE LIBERTY OF HANGIN' WITH OUR HORNED FRIEND FOR A BIT...

TYPICAL YOU, MYR!

YOU'RE OUT DOING WHO-KNOWS-WHAT AND NEVER TELL ANYONE ABOUT IT!

AND YOU, YAGA, CAN'T PASS WIND WITHOUT REPORTING BACK TO THE COVEN ABOUT IT, SO THERE!

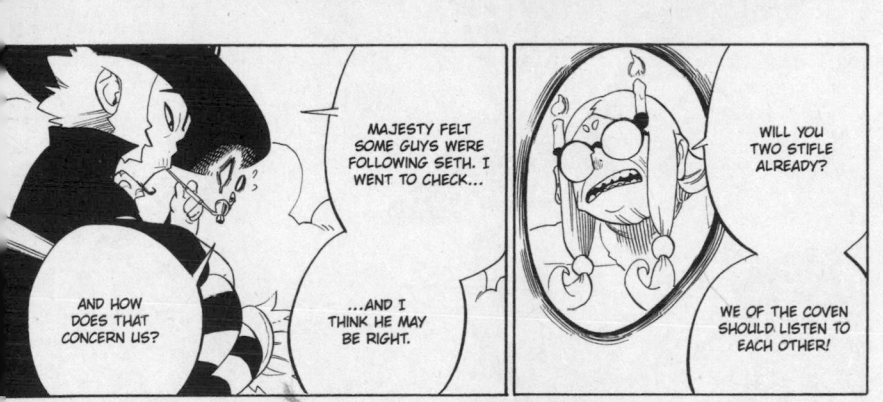

MAJESTY FELT SOME GUYS WERE FOLLOWING SETH. I WENT TO CHECK...

...AND I THINK HE MAY BE RIGHT.

AND HOW DOES THAT CONCERN US?

WILL YOU TWO STIFLE ALREADY?

WE OF THE COVEN SHOULD LISTEN TO EACH OTHER!

YOU THINK IT COULD BE... THE MESNIE?

?!

I DO.

MAJESTY FELT THIS, BUT WASN'T SURE.

HOW MANY WIZARDS DO YOU KNOW WHO COULD GET PAST HIM?

THERE'S JUST NO REASON TO TARGET HIM.

BEATS ME. I JUST WONDER...

BUT WHY WOULD THEY BE AFTER SETH?

MAYBE SO...

HIS INFECTION'S NO BIG DEAL! THEY'RE JUST HORNS!

...THEY WON'T TRY FOR HIM WHILE HE'S THERE. SO HE'LL BE SAFE.

RIGHT NOW, THE KID'S HEADED FOR BÔME. IF THE MESNIE IS AFTER HIM...

BUT IF MEMBERS OF THE MESNIE DO START APPEARING, WE'LL NEED TO GET ORGANIZED!

AS SAFE AS HIDING IN A LION'S DEN TO AVOID A PACK OF HYENAS!

TRUE THAT.

BYE, YAGI-BOO!

WELL, WE'LL LET YOU GET BACK TO IT.

TOODLES!

IF ANYTHING CHANGES, LET ME KNOW!

SO, UH...
MYR?

YEAH?

BE SERIOUS
FOR A
SECOND!

HEY, YOU WANT
A ONE-ON-ONE
WITH URLÄ?
THEN DON'T
CALL ME TOO!

IT'S NOT LIKE
YOU TO ANSWER
THESE CALLS,
Y'KNOW...

CAT GOT YOUR
TONGUE?

GIMME A SEC,
OKAY?!

YGGDRAZILL
TOLD ME...
ABOUT JILL...

AH...

NOPE! WISEST WOULD BE TO STAY FAR AWAY FROM BOME!

ONE OR TWO PLANETS AWAY!

DON'T STRESS, DOC. WE'RE SAFE HERE.

THAT WOULD BE WISEST.

SO, NOW WHAT? HOLD ON AND FREEZE THE REST OF THE TRIP?

LET'S CHECK IT OUT!

BUT IT'S DARK OUTSIDE, AND...

?!

HEY! IS IT ME OR DID SOMETHING PLOP DOWN ON THOSE CABLES?

WATCH OUT! IT'S GONNA...

...CUDDLE US?!

AAAH !!!

SEE HOW AWESOME DRACCOON IS?

YEAH, I MEAN, WE'RE GOOD...

EH... IT'S OKAY...

OKAY?!

HOLD ON, I'LL GET YOU OUTTA THERE!

SHHHH!

"WE'RE SAFE," THEY SAID!

"DON'T WORRY, DOC!"

FEH! WITH OUR TRACK RECORD, WE'RE BOUND TO RUN INTO A HORDE OF INQUISITORS ANY SEC—

HEY! I'M WAY FUN AT PARTIES!

GULP!

WITH ANTISOCIAL MÉLIE GROWLING AT EVERYONE?!

IT SHOULDN'T BE TOO TOUGH TO BLEND INTO THIS CROWD.

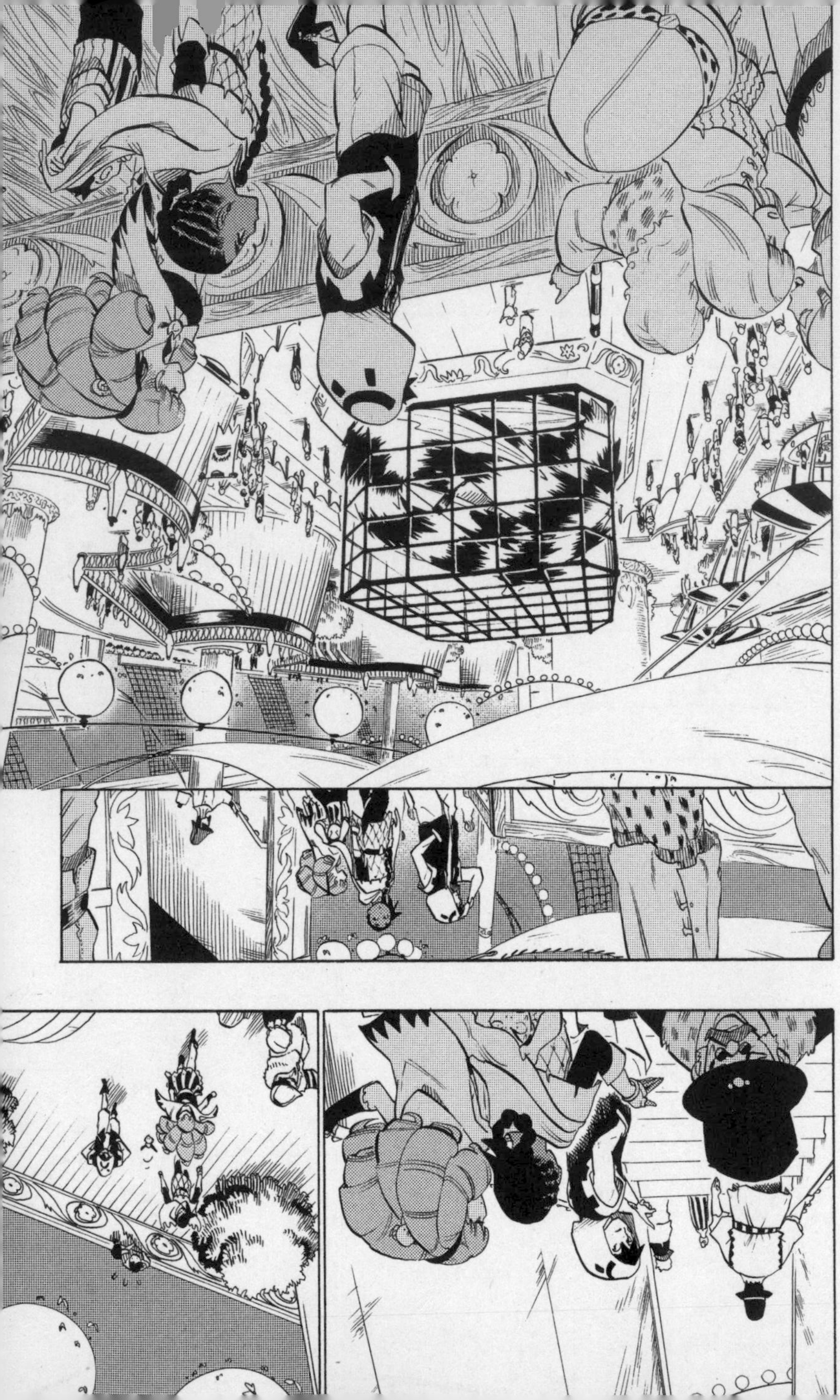

FLOORING?

SECURITY?

CLEANED THIS AFTERNOON, SIR!

CHECKED TWICE, SIR!

UH...

THIS AFTERNOON?!

MY SKYLINER IS THE FASTEST AND MOST LUXURIOUS METHOD OF REACHING VALAY IN BÔME!!

OMIGOSH! IT'S A...A NEME... NEMEME...

A NEMESIS!

JUST DO IT! OUR GUEST OF HONOR WILL BE GRACING US WITH HIS PRESENCE AT THE WINDOW!

BUT IT'LL TAKE AT LEAST A WEEK TO...

EVERYTHING MUST BE SPOTLESS! CLEAN IT ALL AGAIN IN THE NEXT 15 MINUTES!

BUT, SIR...

ENOUGH! IT'S NOT EVERY DAY WE'RE VISITED BY THE REGIONAL GENERAL INQUISITOR!

CHAPTER 82　　　　GENERAL INQUISITOR

SHUSH!

DID HE SAY "GENERAL INQUISI-"

ME FROM AFAR, SETH FROM UP CLOSE.

SO, SETH, YOU'LL NEED TO FIND A HIDING PLACE AND AVOID BEING SEEN.

DOES HE KNOW WHAT YOU ALL LOOK LIKE?

OF ALL THE AIRSHIPS HEADED TOWARDS BÔME...

WHO'D HE SEE DURING THE RUMBLE TOWN ATTACK?

...WE JUST HAD TO CHOOSE THE ONE WITH THAT GUY ON IT!

SETH?

OH, SETH!

NOT ME!

I WOULD LOVE TO HEAR WHY THAT NEMESIS IS ON BOARD.

...AND RETRIEVE THOSE NEMESES...

...SO NOBODY ELSE CAN USE THEM TO KILL MORE PEOPLE!

YOU'RE THE BEST, MÉLIE!

YOU'RE RIGHT... I WAS GOING TO SCREW THINGS UP LIKE I ALWAYS DO...

PFF...

YEAH? WELL, HERE'S A HUG, MÉLIE STYLE!

WHAT?! I JUST WANTED TO GIVE YOU A HUG!

AND YOU CAN BACK OFF, MR. GRABBY!

SHH! WILL YOU TWO KEEP IT DOWN?

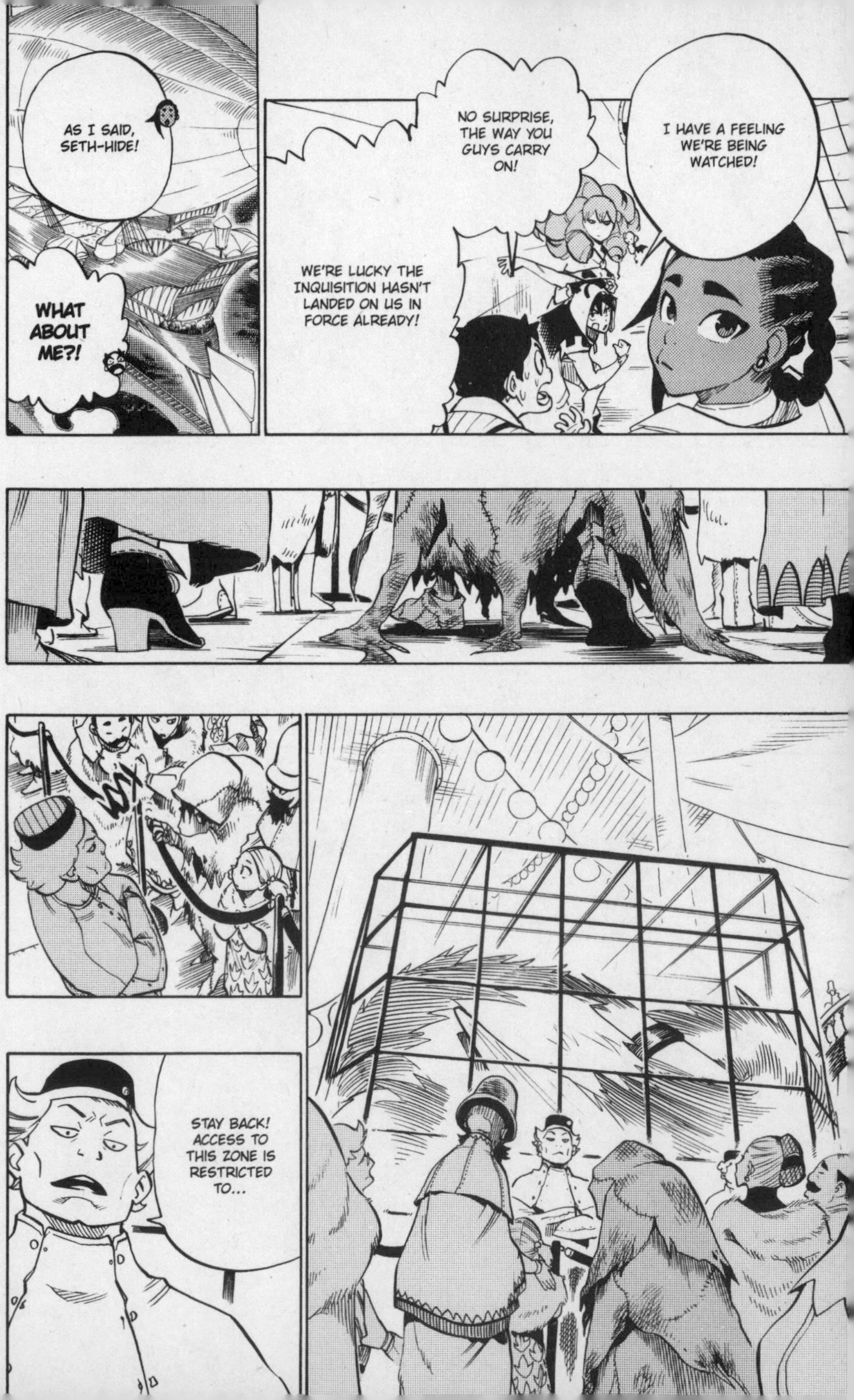

AS I SAID, SETH-HIDE!

WHAT ABOUT ME?!

NO SURPRISE, THE WAY YOU GUYS CARRY ON!

WE'RE LUCKY THE INQUISITION HASN'T LANDED ON US IN FORCE ALREADY!

I HAVE A FEELING WE'RE BEING WATCHED!

STAY BACK! ACCESS TO THIS ZONE IS RESTRICTED TO...

YOU HAVE NOT SEEN ANYTHING.

YOU HAVE NOTHING TO REPORT.

ME NEITHER.

NOTHING TO REPORT.

NOPE.

D'YOU SEE ANYTHING?

THIS DOOR LEADS TO SAFETY, AWAY FROM PRYING EYES.

LEAVE.

THIS DOOR.

LOOK AT ALL THE PEOPLE!

WHERE D'YA RECKON WE SHOULD HIDE?

FINE. I REALLY DON'T WANT TO BUMP INTO ANY INQUISITORS...

IT LEADS TO SAFETY, AWAY FROM PRYING EYES.

HEY, YOU STILL HAVE THOSE ROCKS STUCK IN YOUR PLUMBING?
URGH! YES!
I'VE TRIED TO EJECT THEM, BUT THEY'RE BEING STUBBORN!
EJECT US?! AND THEN WHAT? RETURN TO INFANTILE ANONYMITY?!
NEVER!
HEY, KID! LORDS DON'T RUN AWAY FROM INQUISITORS!
TRUE! A LORD DRAWS HIS BLADE AND CHARGES INTO DANGER!
SO, TELL ME, GUYS... HOW'S LIFE IN THERE?
I MEAN, DEATH, I GUESS...?
YOU ALL **ARE** DEAD, RIGHT?
MAYBE THEY'VE BECOME PART OF YOU.
NO WAY! THEY'RE PARASITES! DOCTORS **HATE** PARASITES!
...
...
HEY, I'M JUST ASKING!

IF TORQUE SPOTS ANYTHING, EVEN FROM A DISTANCE, IT'LL BE THAT!

QUICK! HIDE YOUR HAIR!

THE GENERAL INQUISITOR'S ARRIVING!

?!

HEY!

SIR.

YOU! SCRAM!

YOU'RE EARLY! MY APOLOGIES FOR NOT BEING READY TO GREET YOU!

GENERAL!

NO...

HUH... DOC TOLD ME TORQUE WAS A BIG GUY WITH RED HAIR...

MAYBE THAT OLD KID'S COLOR BLIND?

I DO NOT UNDERSTAND.
A LIVE NEMESIS ABOARD A VESSEL FILLED WITH CIVILIANS...
SO THIS IS THE NEMESIS THAT YOU ARE TRANSPORTING TO THE CAPITAL OF THE ESTRIE KINGDOMS?
CORRECT!
IT WAS AN ORDER FROM THE BÔME INQUISITION!
THEY ARE CURRENTLY TRANSPORTING LIVE SPECIMENS THROUGHOUT THE REGION.
TO WHAT PURPOSE?
WELL, I'M NOT AT LIBERTY TO S-
THEY WANT TO PUT THEM ON DISPLAY.
?

IT IS GOOD TO KNOW...

...THAT OUR SAFETY DOES NOT DEPEND ON INFECTED!

BUT AT WHAT PRICE?

TO SHOW THEY CAN DO WITHOUT WIZARDS.

...THEY HOPE TO PROVE THE EFFICIENCY OF SAME.

BY DISPLAYING NEMESES CAPTURED BY INQUISITION FORCES...

...BUT THEY SIMPLY AREN'T AS EFFECTIVE AS WIZARDS AND THEIR SPELLS.

THEY PROVIDE GOOD OFFENSE AGAINST NEMESES AND THEIR FANTASIA...

WHITE AND BLACK SILVER ARE HIDEOUSLY EXPENSIVE.

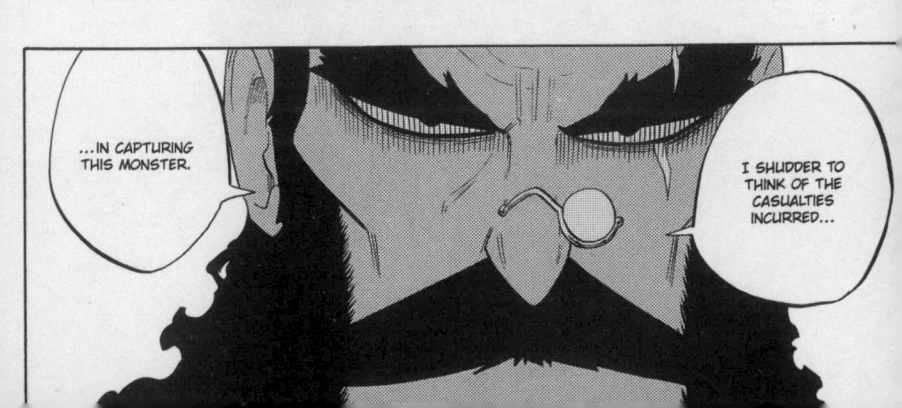

...IN CAPTURING THIS MONSTER.

I SHUDDER TO THINK OF THE CASUALTIES INCURRED...

THE MARSHAL HAS ORDERED ALL THE MOST INFLUENTIAL INQUISITORS ACROSS PHARÉNOS TO CONVENE...

...IN ORDER TO ASSESS MATTERS IN THE AFTERMATH OF THE CYFANDIR WAR.

IT LOOKS LIKE THIS SPECTACLE COINCIDES PERFECTLY WITH THE ASSEMBLY.

IS THAT WHY YOU'RE TRAVELING WITH US?

OUR FINAL DESTINATION IS THE COUNCIL OF GENERALS IN BÔME.

WE REALLY MUST KEEP OUR HEADS DOWN!

...

A COUNCIL OF INQUISITION GENERALS?

CHAPTER 83

SIDE EFFECTS

WELL, YOU SUGGESTED THAT DOOR!

IT'S TOO QUIET!

WHEN YOU DO WE END UP IN A WORSE SITUATION THAN BEFORE!

AND YOU LISTENED TO ME?!

I'M TAKING YOUR ADVICE AND **NOT** LISTENING TO YOU!

NO!

LET'S GO BACK!

BUT...!

CALM DOWN, OKAY? I KNOW YOU'RE SCARED...

YEAH, I AM NOW, BUT BEFORE...

...BUT YOU'RE STILL ALIVE, AREN'T YOU?

DRACCOON'S GOT TEN TIMES MORE MEAT ON 'IM!

BUT THAT THING JUST HAD TO CHOOSE THE RUNT OF THE GROUP!

AND WHAT DISH DOES HE PICK FOR LUNCH, EH?

I MEAN, THAT GIANT SQUID WAS HUNGRY...

THIS GUY!

YUH-DUH! AND YOU SHOULD TOO!

SO YOU THINK EVERYTHING'S OUT TO GET YOU?

AS IF I EVER COUNTED ON THAT!

AND DON'T COUNT ON OL' DOC TO COME TO YOUR RESCUE!

YOU CAN USE SPELLS WITHOUT TOOLS...

BUT YOU'LL SEE! EVENTUALLY YOU'LL GET CAUGHT!

OH, PISH!

BUT YEARS IN A DAY? THAT'S WHAT-

LIKE, WHAT IF IT STARTED AGING ME WITH NO WAY TO STOP IT?

SIDE EFFECTS? LIKE WHAT?

I JUST WANTED TO MAKE SURE OF ANY SIDE EFFECTS BEFORE DRINKING MORE OF IT.

HEY, WE'RE ALL AGING.

WELL... YEAH...

BOOM

FFFF

AW, GET IT OVER WITH!

NOT ALL AT... GLUG!

GLP

FWIT

...TO THOSE WHO TRAVEL FIRST CLASS.

THAT IS TRUE.

I HAVE OBSERVED THAT NO DOORS ARE ACTUALLY CLOSED...

...ABOARD A LUXURY VESSEL.

EVEN A NEMESIS IS ALLOWED TO TRAVEL ALL THE WAY TO BÔME...

I'M SURE IT ENJOYS DOING SO.

BÉLÉLÉ

I HOPE IT'S TO YOUR TASTE!

GRR

ER... LOOK OVER HERE, GENERAL!

I PICKED OUT THIS FLORA DÉCOR MYSELF!

CHAPTER 84

CORROSIVE

WHAT'RE YOU AFTER, HAG?
I RECKON SHE'S UP TO NO GOOD!
YOU DON' THAY!
SHE SAID SOMETHING ABOUT A MOUTH-WATERING ABILITY!
LIKE HANDLING FANTASIA BAREHANDED?
SO YOU CAME TO...
SILENCE!
...
ALERT! ALERT! ALERT!
BLOODY HELL!
IT SEEMS MY SUGGESTIONS DON'T WORK... I'LL HAVE TO TRY SOMETHING ELSE.

LET IT GO, WE'LL TAKE CARE OF IT!
WE'RE FLYING OVER AN INHABITED AREA! NO WAY I'LL LET A NEMESIS LOOSE HERE!
NO! LET IT GO!
SO YOU'LL LET IT KILL EVERYONE ABOARD THIS SHIP?!
MY... MY AIRSHIP!
CATASTROPHE!!
SHH!...
HH!...

PULSAR'S EXHAUSTED! CAN'T KEEP FENDING HER OFF!

I THOUGHT IT WAS ME SHE WANTED!

YOU CAN USE SPELLS WITHOUT TOOLS... EVENTUALLY YOU'LL GET CAUGHT!

OH NO! NOW THAT I HAVE YOU... I'M KEEPING YOU!

WHY'S SHE AFTER DOC?

HEY, CORPSE LADY! I'M NOT DONE WITH YOU!

THE EATHS WITHARDS?!

ONE OF THE MANY INFECTIONS I'VE SAVORED...FROM THE FLESH OF TASTY WIZARDS!

I DON'T THINK I'VE EVER HEARD OF ANYONE WITH A USEFUL INFECTION BEFORE.

I HOPE IT'S BENIGN AND EASY TO LIVE WITH.

I DON'T KNOW YET.

SO, WHAT'S YOUR INFECTION?

THEY JUST DISAPPEARED.

ANYONE WHO DID HAVE ONE IS ALREADY GONE.

I MOLT!

SO I GUESS THAT'S MY INFECTION–

?!

WHERE ARE
YOU?!

MÉLIE!
OCOHO!

THE NEMESIS
ESCAPED AND
GRABBED A
GIRL!

WE CHASED
IT TO THE
TOP OF THE
BALLOON...

SETH!
FINALLY!

OCOHO,
LISTEN!
DOC'S...

MÉLIE
DISAPPEARED!

...

?!

SHE WAS STANDING RIGHT NE—

I DON'T KNOW HOW, BUT MÉLIE JUST DISAPPEARED!

WE WANTED TO SAVE THE GIRL AND...

PWII!

OCOHO? OCOHO!

OCOHO! WHAT'S HAPPENING?!

WUSH!

AND THE
OTHERS?!

WHERE'S THE
NEMESIS?

I...

TWO GIRLS
WERE AFTER THE
NEMESIS! WHERE
ARE THEY?!

?

HEY,
YOU!

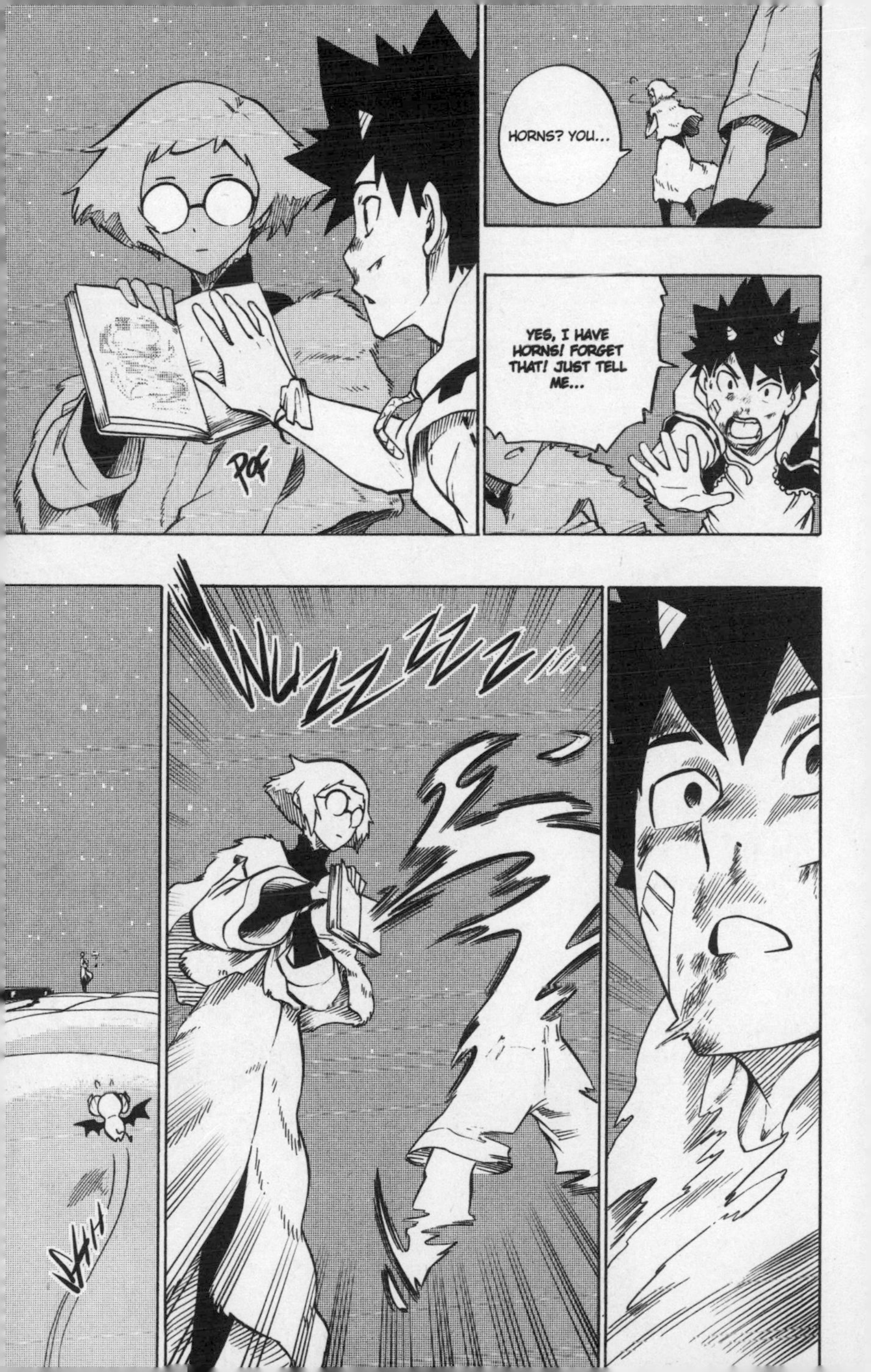

HORNS? YOU...

YES, I HAVE
HORNS! FORGET
THAT! JUST TELL
ME...

BUT I'D NO IDEA I'D RUN INTO THE HORNED WIZARD ALONG THE WAY.

IT WOULD HAVE BEEN SAFER TO ACQUIRE THE NEMESIS WHEN WE REACHED BÔME...

LUPA LYCCO
–DOMITOR WIZARD–

TO BE CONTINUED...

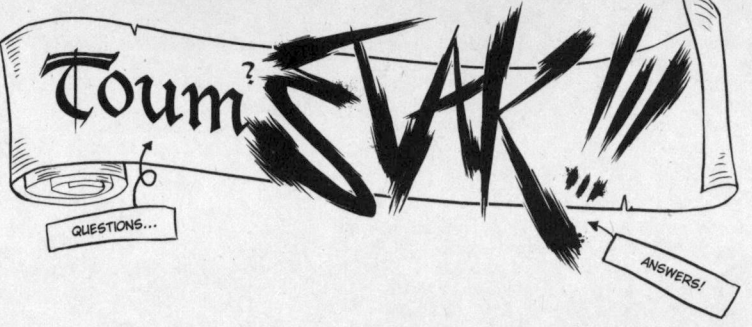

Cap'tain Gautan: Hi Tony. First of all, I wanted to thank you and congratulate you on your manga that I love! It's quickly become my favorite manga and is a big source of inspiration to me! I love writing stories myself by taking inspiration from things I see/read and I have a couple of questions. How do you write a character who is intelligent, a lot more so than yourself, for example? Personally, I have a bit of difficulty becoming smarter than I already am, in order to write my character. ^^'

Tony Valente: The best thing to do is of course to research as much as possible his field of specialty, to be able to give more detailed elements when the moment arises and to try to think differently when you embody him. Me, I try to imagine standing in every one of my characters' shoes when I write, and I even surprise myself when I notice that I start thinking differently in those cases. I'd say it's probably a job very close to actors' when they need to embody a character themselves! So, you need to think hard about defining your character's personality and know from what angle we perceive their intelligence. Do their actions have a certain rationale behind them? Are they cool-headed? Or, maybe they act fast but seem like they have everything thought through in advance? Or even yet, they might be pedantic? There are a lot of ways to show that your character is smart, so just find the right angle!

– In *Radiant,* and especially in volume 4, what I really think is extremely well done are the dialogue and the choice of words! I'd like to know your secret for writing such powerful dialogue that still stays with me to this day!

Thanks! ^^ I'm not too sure about what makes or breaks a scene, but when your characters are really motivated and convinced to their very core of something, then the confrontation that comes from that can be quite enriching. An argument only gains in weight when confronted with an opposite one. Heroes need to confront arguments that unsettle their own. By doing so, as they persist in defending their own beliefs, it gives them more strength! And don't forget that adversaries are also the heroes of their own stories. They also need to be able to convince, even if they're wrong! It all depends on the choice of words in the dialogue. The more precise you are, the less you'll need to have them use long sentences and the more opportunity you'll have of creating a big impact!

- Finally, I wanted to know how long you hope to continue doing *Radiant*.
No idea, but I know it's not anywhere near finished!

....

Baptiste: Hello hello! I have an important question related to the understanding of volume 6 of *Radiant*: where did Myr's boxers disappear to in chapter 40?
Tony Valente: He put them in his pocket. They're not the correct size when he's in that shape.

....

Victor B.: Toum, toum, ba-toum!!! I have a couple of new questions for you: by whom, how and from what is Pen Draig's armor made out of?
Tony Valente: That will surely be addressed at one point in the manga...

- Is it possible (besides in Seth's exceptional case) to find the same Infection twice in the world of *Radiant*?
It is, yes.

- How did you go about making the map of Pharénos at the beginning of volume 5? Did you get some help or did you come up with it yourself?

I studied some old maps for a while and also looked into Heraldry for a bit (the study of armorial bearings) to see what gave it its authenticity and charm... Because yeah, I think old maps and crests are cute, okay? It makes me all tingly, I don't know why... So I jotted down some elements that inspired me and then I created one myself, based on some notes of places I wanted to show in the story. And then I just freewheeled here, twisted some things there, over the span of a couple days!!

- I noticed that Doc is one of the only main characters to not have gotten his own volume cover yet. Is it because he's not charismatic enough?

Actually, he's on the cover of volume 9, and based on the badassery counter established by my readers, he should even be on top! But, yeah, I have to admit I was kind of waiting for the right time to put him on a cover...^^

....

Nourpoke: Alright, so it's kind of basic, but I first calmly wanted to say that I LOOOOOOOOOOOOOOOOOOOOVE *RADIANT* (just about...this much).
I also have four questions (if this is you, Tony... Sir? I dunno!) that I would love for you to answer. Do you take inspiration from anything in particular for the whole vibe of the world and the visuals of *Radiant*? (Because really, great job on those!)

Tony Valente: It depends. Rumble Town was 100 percent made up, Caislean Merlin is very much based on Celtic culture for certain aspects and European architecture. But in general, I just look at a lot of references of places I like, to find some small details here and there I could reuse!

- How many volumes have you drawn up/prepared the scenario for, Tony? I mean, sir! (Because if it stops, I think I might have no reason to live!)

I have the story outline mapped out, but I don't have a definite number of volumes in mind!

- Being a high school student, I'm looking into art (drawing) schools for when I graduate. So I'd love it if you could tell me which one you went to (because I'm drawing a blank here...).

I did not go to school for this, so I can't recommend anything!

- When are tufrlbredc...? And don't make me repeat myself! I hate that!

You too? This is becoming a real epidemic!!

....

Nicolas L.: Hello Tony! My name is Nicolas and I wanted to know, since there's already an anime adaptation of this (wonderful) manga, if there'll also be a video game adaptation? I'd be so happy if there was one. In the meantime I'll just patiently wait for the next volume. Keep up the great work! :D

Tony Valente: There is nothing planned as of yet, and just between you and me, I'd be very surprised if there was! Better not get your hopes up! But if there's ever a possibility to get one, I'd love that, of course! ^^

....

Alban H.: Hello Mr. Valente, I wanted to say that I love the way you handle each single character in your manga, especially the women. Actually, compared to certain other, big name manga series, I feel like you take the time to develop your female characters and give them as much importance as your male characters. My question, however, relates to a male character: is the Inquisitor/Thaumaturge Von Teppes still alive? I don't remember reading anything about him ever since volume 4. Good luck for the rest of the adventure and farewell!

Tony Valente: Ah! Well, that is really nice to hear, thank you for that comment! I try to handle all my characters with as much care, whether they're male or female, and if you noticed that then I'm really happy!! And to answer your question... No, which will be addressed at a certain point!

....

Lilou Rebel: Hello Mister Valente, I really enjoy reading *Radiant* ever since its first volumes and always delighted to go buy the newest volume when it's released. I understood that in the beginning the series was supposed to end after 3 volumes, but that didn't happen and I'm very happy about it. But why have you stopped giving each volume its own little bit of personality? So as to spread out the information? Before, every volume contained very

intriguing bits of information and would try to complete part of the series. I loved that! That finished feeling, and the "French" jokes added here and there, would always give the story a little bit of humor and everything would fit together perfectly and we'd learn something new every time. Now, I'm wondering, was this on purpose?

Tony Valente: I treat story in terms of arcs. Volume 1 works by itself, but then volumes 2 to 4 consist of the Rumble Town arc, and volumes 5 to 10 are the Wizard-Knight arc. From my point of view, it's not just one volume that makes the identity of a series, it's the arcs. Since the arcs have been getting longer, it takes a little longer to provide any new reveals! As for the jokes, however, that depends on the scene, but I don't think I've stopped putting in any :)

- Did Seth get a growth spurt in between volumes by any chance? ^^

Yes! Actually, no. But I drew him a little too young in volume 1 compared to the image I had of him. So gradually, until volume 4, I'd been aging him a little to the point that he was closer to the mental image I had! There was also another reason. When he left Alma, he became a little more autonomous and responsible, and I wanted people to feel that through the art. Also, my art style's changed a little, so that also plays a role!

- Will we be getting any tournaments in *Radiant* in the future? (or was the 56th Wizardry Championship only shown for effect?)

I don't think so, no. But then again, the story isn't over yet, so maybe in a few years!

PS: By the way, thank you as well for Doc (who is my favorite character), because not only is he hilarious, he's now also looking really cool!

Thank you! I had planned this for a while now, and I'm happy to finally have been able to show him in this armor! ^^

....

Raphaël L.: Hi Tony, my name is Raphaël and I love *Radiant*, the series is just brilliant!!!! How did you come up with the concept for *Radiant*?

Tony Valente: I gathered a lot of ideas and all these things I wanted to do since I was young, I mixed it all up and BAM, that's how *Radiant* got made!

- Are you going to write any other manga besides *Radiant*?

I hope so! But not anytime soon…

- Are we going to see any couples amongst the Inquisitors? What about Seth and his group?

Well, ehhh… No idea! The characters all live out their own lives, I'm just going along with them…

- Will you be doing any signing sessions in France? If so, when and where?

Every year I go to Japan Expo in Paris. Besides that, I don't have anything else in my schedule, but that could change. I share all this info on Facebook as soon as it gets finalized.

- Can you give us a top 5 of your favorite characters?

Oh, that's a tough one… Mmm… No, no matter how I try to think about it, I just can't do it.

....

Lélia G.: Hello Tony, thank you so much for all the work you're doing! *Radiant* really is such a fun series to read! I had a question: can animals become Infected and use the Fantasia? It'd be so wicked to see a Wizard Camel!

Tony Valente: Humans and animals have different reactions when they're touched by a Nemesis. I hope to be able to talk more about this in future volumes!

Cédric E.: Hi Tony! A few months ago I asked you if you were able to tie a double tie like Doc, and I finally found a rather easy way to do it, so I tried making a tutorial. Although I'm not sure I used the right terminology or the correct phrases for the written part, I did what I could.

Tony Valente: Well, here we go!! Dear readers, I present to you… The secret of Doc's Double Tie!

STEP 1: TIE A REGULAR TIE AROUND YOUR NECK.

STEP 2: TIE ANOTHER ONE AROUND THE COLLAR OF THE FIRST ONE.

STEP 3: ADJUST.

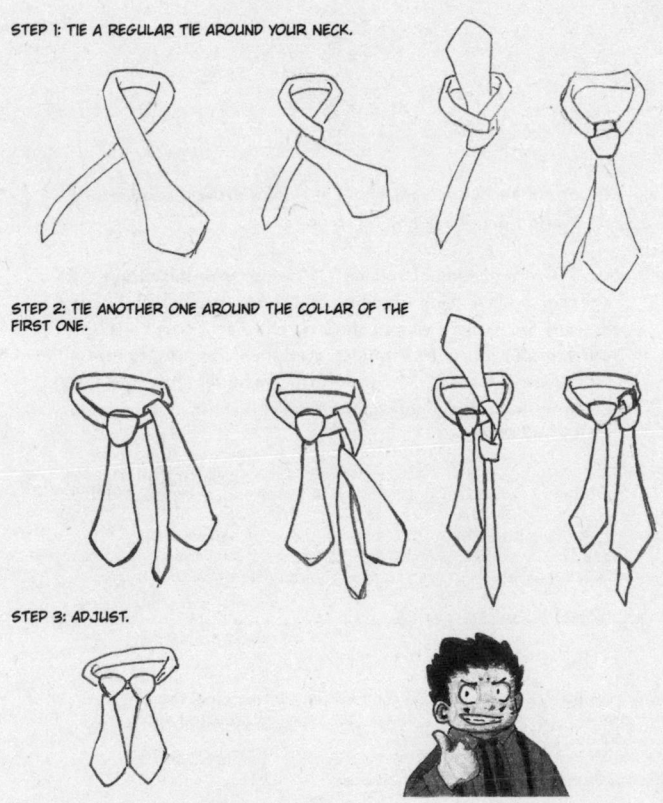

Me, at the end of volume 10: "I'm gonna draw a broom race à la Mario Kart! It's gonna be so cool!"

Me, at the beginning of volume 11: "I'm so over this already!" Why did I even think of doing a broom race when I hate contests! Seriously! I was so stuck on chapter 77, so I just had Seth vent out all my frustration... And then came Taj to nicely make sense of all of this. So grateful to him for that. It's moments like these that I really notice that there're just too many people living in my head.

—Tony Valente

Tony Valente began working as a comic artist with the series *The Four Princes of Ganahan*, written by Raphael Drommelschlager. He then launched a new three-volume project, *Hana Attori*, after which he produced *S.P.E.E.D. Angels*, a series written by Didier Tarquin and colored by Pop.

In preparation for *Radiant*, he relocated to Canada. Through confronting caribou and grizzlies, he gained the wherewithal to train in obscure manga techniques. Since then, his eating habits have changed, his lifestyle became completely different and even his singing voice has changed a bit!

RADIANT VOL. 11
VIZ MEDIA Manga Edition

STORY AND ART BY **TONY VALENTE**
ASSISTANT ARTIST **TPIU**

Translation/**(´・∀・`)ｻﾌﾟ?**
Touch-Up Art & Lettering/**Erika Terriquez**
Design/**Julian [JR] Robinson**
Editor/**Gary Leach**

Published by arrangement with MEDIATOON LICENSING/Ankama.
RADIANT T11
© ANKAMA EDITIONS 2019, by Tony Valente
All rights reserved

Printed in the U.S.A.

Published by VIZ Media, LLC
P.O. Box 77010
San Francisco, CA 94107

10 9 8 7 6 5 4 3 2 1
First printing, May 2020

viz.com

PARENTAL ADVISORY
RADIANT is rated T for Teen and is recommended for ages 13 and up. This volume contains fantasy violence.

Kidnapped by the Demon King and imprisoned in his castle, Princess Syalis is...bored.

Sleepy Princess in the Demon Castle

Story & Art by
KAGIJI KUMANOMATA

Captured princess Syalis decides to while away her hours in the Demon Castle by sleeping, but getting a good night's rest turns out to be a lot of work! She begins by fashioning a DIY pillow out of the fur of her Teddy Demon guards and an "air mattress" from the magical Shield of the Wind. Things go from bad to worse—for her captors—when some of Princess Syalis's schemes end in her untimely—if temporary—demise and she chooses the Forbidden Grimoire for her bedtime reading...

YOU'RE READING THE WRONG WAY

RADIANT reads from right to left, starting in the upper-right corner, meaning that action, sound effects, and word-balloon order are completely reversed from English order.